DEVELOPING LITERACY

Photocopiable teaching resources

UNDERSTANDING AND RESPONDING TO TEXTS

Ages 8–9

Christine Moorcroft

A & C Black • London

Published 2008 by A & C Black Publishers Limited
38 Soho Square, London W1D 3HB
www.acblack.com

ISBN 978-0-7136-8463-6

Copyright text © Christine Moorcroft 2008
Copyright illustrations © KJA Artists 2008
Copyright cover illustration © Piers Baker 2008
Editor: Jane Klima
Designed by Susan McIntyre

The author and publishers would like to thank Ray Barker and Rifat Siddiqui for their
advice in producing this series of books.

A CIP catalogue record for this book is available from the British Library.

he authors and publishers are grateful for permission to reproduce the following:

p.14: From *The Thieves of Ostia* by Caroline Lawrence. Reproduced by permission of
Orion. p. 23: From *On The Run* by Elizabeth Laird. Reproduced by permission of
Egmont UK. p. 27: From *The Girl Who Stayed For Half A Week* by Gene Kemp.
Reproduced by permission of Faber and Faber. p.32: From *A Bad Beginning* by
Lemony Snicket. Reproduced by permission of Egmont UK. p.61-62: From 'Witch
Witch' by Rose Fyleman. Reproduced by permission of The Society of Authors.
From 'The Doll Festival' by James Kirkup. Reproduced by permission of the author.
'Thanksgiving' from *Cherry Stones! Garden Swings!* by Ivy O. Eastwick. Reproduced
by permission of The United Methodist Publishing House. Every effort has been
made to trace copyright holders and to obtain their permission for use of copyright
material. The authors and publishers would be pleased to rectify any error or omission
in future editions.

Printed by Halstan Printing Group, Amersham, Buckinghamshire.

A & C Black uses paper produced with elemental chlorine-free pulp, harvested from
managed sustainable forests.

Contents

Introduction

100% New Developing Literacy Understanding and Responding to Texts is a series of seven photocopiable activity books for developing children's responses to different types of text and their understanding of the structure and purposes of different types of text.

The books provide learning activities to support strands 7 and 8 (Understanding and interpreting texts and Engaging with and responding to texts) of the literacy objectives of the Primary Framework for Literacy and Mathematics.

The structure of *100% New Developing Literacy Understanding and Responding to Texts: Ages 8–9* complements the structure of the Primary Framework and includes the range of text types suggested in the planning for activities for children aged 8–9. It focuses on the following types of text:

- Narrative (stories with historical settings, stories set in imaginary worlds, stories from other cultures, stories that raise issues or dilemmas, plays)
- Non-fiction (recounts: newspapers and magazines, information texts, explanations, persuasive texts)
- Poetry (creating images, exploring form).

100% New Developing Literacy Understanding and Responding to Texts: Ages 8–9 addresses the following learning objectives from the Primary Framework for Literacy:

Strand 7 Understanding and interpreting texts

- Identify and summarise evidence from a text to support a hypothesis
- Deduce characters' reasons for behaviour from their actions and explain how ideas are developed in non-fiction texts
- Use knowledge of different organisational features of texts to find information effectively
- Use knowledge of word structures and origins to develop their understanding of word meanings
- Explain how writers use figurative and expressive language to create images and atmosphere.

Strand 8 Engaging with and responding to texts

- Read extensively favourite authors or genres and experiment with other types of text
- Interrogate texts to deepen and clarify understanding and response
- Explore why and how writers write, including through face-to-face and online contact with authors.

The activities

Some of the activities can be carried out with the whole class, some are more suitable for small groups and others are for individual work. It is important that the children are encouraged to enjoy stories and poetry – not just to learn about how they are written – and that they have opportunities to listen to, repeat, learn, recite and join in poems for enjoyment. Many of the activities can be adapted for use at different levels, to suit the differing levels of attainment of the children (see the Teachers' notes on the page). Several can be used in different ways as explained in the *Notes on the activities* (see page 6).

Reading

Most children will be able to carry out the activities independently but some of them will need help in reading some of the instructions on the sheets. It is expected that someone will read them to or with them, if necessary.

Organisation

The activities require very few resources besides pencils, crayons, scissors and glue. Other materials are specified in the Teachers' notes on the pages: for example, fiction, poetry or information books, websites and CD-ROMs.

Extension activities

Most of the activity sheets end with a challenge (*Now try this!*) which reinforces and extends the children's learning. These more challenging activities might be appropriate for only a few children; it is not expected that the whole class should complete them, although many more children might benefit from them with appropriate  assistance – possibly as a guided or shared activity. On some pages there is space for the children to complete the extension activities, but others will require a notebook or a separate sheet of paper.

Accompanying CD

The enclosed CD-ROM contains all the activity sheets from the book and allows you to edit them for printing or saving. This means that modifications can be made to differentiate the activities further to suit individual pupils' needs. See page 12 for further details.

Notes on the activities

The notes below expand upon those which are provided at the bottom of the activity pages. They give ideas for making the most of the activity, including suggestions for the whole-class introduction, the plenary session or for follow-up work using an adapted version of the sheet. To help teachers to select appropriate learning experiences for their pupils, the activities are grouped into sections within each book but the pages need not be presented in the order in which they appear, unless stated otherwise.

Stories and poems featured or suggested in this book and supplementary texts

Stories with historical settings:
Doodlebug Summer (Alison Prince, A & C Black *Flashbacks* series)
Mission to Marathon (Geoffrey Trease, A & C Black *Flashbacks* series)
A Candle in the Dark (Adèle Geras, A & C Black *Flashbacks* series)
Across the Roman Wall (Theresa Breslin, A & C Black *Flashbacks* series)
A Ghost-Light in the Attic (Pat Thomson, A & C Black *Flashbacks* series)
The Thieves of Ostia (Caroline Lawrence, Orion *The Roman Mysteries* series)
The Secrets of Vesuvius (Caroline Lawrence, Orion *The Roman Mysteries* series)
The Pirates of Pompeii (Caroline Lawrence, Orion *The Roman Mysteries* series)
The Assassins of Rome (Caroline Lawrence, Orion *The Roman Mysteries* series)
The Dolphins of Laurentum (Caroline Lawrence, Orion *The Roman Mysteries* series)
The Twelve Tasks of Flavia Gemina (Caroline Lawrence, Orion *The Roman Mysteries* series)
Carrie's War (Nina Bawden, Puffin)
Keeping Henry (Nina Bawden, Puffin)
The Wolves of Willoughby Chase (Joan Aiken, Puffin)
The Dancing Bear (Peter Dickinson, Puffin)
Moonfleet (J. Meade Falkner, Puffin)
Smith (Leon Garfield, Puffin)
The Wool Pack (Cynthia Harnett, Puffin)
The Eagle of the Ninth (Rosemary Sutcliffe, Puffin)
The Machine Gunners (Robert Westall, Puffin)
Little House in the Big Woods (Laura Ingalls Wilder, Puffin)

Stories set in imaginary worlds:
Harry Potter series (J. K. Rowling, Bloomsbury)
The Railway Children (Edith Nesbit, Penguin)
The Wind in the Willows (Kenneth Grahame, Penguin)
The Winter Sleepwalker (Joan Aiken, Red Fox)
Whizziwig (Malorie Blackman, A & C Black)
Whizziwig Returns (Malorie Blackman, A & C Black)
The Dragon's Child (Jenny Nimmo, Mammoth)
The BFG (Roald Dahl, Puffin)
The Mouse and His Child (Russell Hoban, Puffin)
Charmed Life (Diana Wynne Jones, Puffin)
The Wizard of Earthsea (Ursula Le Guin, Puffin)

Stories from other cultures:
On the Run (Elizabeth Laird, Mammoth)
Abdullah's Butterfly (Janine M. Fraser, HarperCollins)
Grace and Family (Mary Hoffman, Frances Lincoln)
Tales from Africa (Mary Medlicott, Kingfisher)

Stories that raise issues or dilemmas:
The Girl Who Stayed For Half a Week (from *Roundabout*, Gene Kemp, Faber & Faber)
Dinosaurs and All That Rubbish (Michael Foreman, Puffin)
Project Kite (Sian Lewis, Red Fox)
Brother Eagle, Sister Sky (Chief Seattle, Puffin)
Free the Whales (Jamie Rix, Walker)
Badger's Parting Gifts (Susan Varley, HarperCollins)
Little Obie and the Flood (Martin Waddell, Walker)
Tales of a Fourth Grade Nothing (Judy Blume, Random House)
Down and Out (Bernard Ashley, Orchard)
The Bad Beginning (Lemony Snicket, Egmont)

Play scripts:
The Boy Who Fell into a Book (Alan Ayckbourn, Faber)
Grimm Tales (Carol Ann Supple & Tim Supple, Scholastic)
Whale (David Holman, Heinemann)
Curtain Up series (A & C Black)
Bill's New Frock (Anne Fine, Longman)
Two Weeks with the Queen (Morris Gleitzman, Macmillan)
The Turbulent Term of Tyke Tiler (Gene Kemp, Heinemann)
The Wind in the Willows (Kenneth Grahame, Adapted by Alan Bennett, Faber)

Useful books of poems:
The Works (chosen by Paul Cookson, Macmillan)
The Works 2 (chosen by Brian Moses & Pie Corbett, Macmillan)
I Like This Poem (chosen by Kaye Webb, Puffin)
Shades of Green (chosen by Anne Harvey, Red Fox)
Welcome to the Party (chosen by Nicola Davies & Simon Rae, BBC)
The Hutchinson Treasury of Children's Poetry (edited by Alison Sage, Hutchinson)
The Kingfisher Book of Children's Poetry (selected by Michael Rosen, Kingfisher)
The Puffin Book of Twentieth-Century Children's Verse (edited by Brian Patten, Puffin)

Useful websites
Narrative/plays:
http://www.bbc.co.uk/cbbc/romanmysteries/game/index.shtml (Caroline Lawrence's series *The Roman Mysteries*)
http://www.screenonline.org.uk/tv/id/562525/index.html (*The Railway Children*)
http://www.whirligig-tv.co.uk/tv/children/other/railway_children.htm (*The Railway Children*)
www.bibliomania.com
www.fablevision.com
www.literature.org
www.storiesfromtheweb.org

This book is divided into three main sections: **Narrative**, **Non-fiction** and **Poetry**. These are sub-divided to match the Planning Units of the Primary Framework for Literacy.

Narrative

Stories with historical settings

> The activities in this section are about stories set in the past: some of them feature periods from history that will be familiar to the children through their work in history lessons. Some passages from well-known children's books are featured. These could serve as 'tasters' to encourage the children to read the books for themselves or the longer ones could be read in serial form as shared texts. In this way you can encourage the children to develop preferences and to read extensively their favourite authors in this genre.

In the past (page 13) helps the children to identify the clues that tell them about the time and place setting of a story. They should notice that Carrie remembers events from thirty years earlier – the story is told using 'flashback' techniques. Focus on the techniques in order to help the children to explore how authors write. This could be linked with work in history on the Second World War.

A historical setting (page 14) focuses on the use of vivid descriptive details to evoke another time and place. Focus on the techniques in order to help the children to explore how authors write. They will need access to good dictionaries to look up the meanings of some of the words or you could provide a copy of the book the passage is from; this and the other books in *The Roman Mysteries* series provide a glossary. You could also link this with work on the meanings of words; explain that the name Gemina means twin: Flavia's family name is the feminine form of her father's name Geminus (he is a twin). Link this to the meaning of the zodiac sign Gemini and to work on plurals of words derived from Latin, also to work in history on Invaders (the Romans).

Past talk (page 15) features words, phrases and idioms which have dropped out of use and have been replaced by others, particularly in colloquial language: for example, nowadays the expressions *young rip*, *young gentleman* and *beastly* sound old-fashioned, although the children will have no difficulty in understanding them. The idiom *Tell that to the Marines* (derived from *Tell that to the horse-marines*) is a joke phrase – there was never any such thing as 'horse-marines' – and means *Don't expect me to believe that!* Other obsolete expressions include *for a lark* (for fun), *not much lark* (not much fun) and *you are a brick* (you are kind/understanding). Ask the children to share other words and phrases that they consider old-fashioned. Discuss whether they need to understand every reference or word in historical texts to enjoy the story. Draw out that the contemporary texts that they read and write will one day be regarded as using obsolete expressions.

Historical clues (page 16) develops skills in gathering information about features of stories with historical settings (for suggested texts, see the list on page 6). The children are encouraged to notice details which are related to the setting, are different from modern settings and help the reader to imagine the setting. Focus on the techniques in order to help the children to explore how authors write. They could prepare to write their own story in a historical setting by researching the place and way of life at the time and the people who might have lived there.

Look and listen (page 17) focuses on television adaptations of stories with historical settings. The children could also compare the television version with the book (for suggested texts, see the list on page 6).

Stories set in imaginary worlds

> These activities focus on the ways in which authors create imaginary worlds and evoke their atmospheres, on the ways in which characters respond to these settings and how the author communicates the characters' responses.

The world of Harry Potter (page 18) is about the way in which the author J. K. Rowling develops the imaginary world over the course of the series of seven books. Focus on the techniques in order to help the children to explore how authors write. It is suggested that the children work in groups, with different children concentrating on different books, depending on which ones they have read. Those who have not read any of them could begin reading the first book as either a shared or individual reading activity. Some children who have read the entire series might be able to record for themselves all the pieces of information they discover from each new book. They could also write a chapter featuring themselves as characters.

Atmospheric (page 19) focuses on how the author creates the atmosphere of a setting and prepares the reader for the events of the chapter. Focus on the techniques in order to help the children to explore how authors write. You could draw out the closeness of the characters to nature around the riverbank in *The Wind in the Willows*. The children could also select passages, from books they are reading, that evoke an atmosphere especially well and talk about the kinds of events the atmosphere seemed to foretell and how well this matched what actually happened. The children could change the first passage as in this example: *The shiny white tiled floor glared up at the brilliant white ceiling; the stainless steel chairs, gleaming from recent polishing...*

Characters in settings (page 20) focuses on how the setting of a story affects the actions of a character. The children are encouraged to imagine that characters they know from stories are faced with different settings and to predict how they will respond. Ask them to explain their ideas and to give evidence from stories they have read. They could also write notes to prepare a chapter featuring themselves as characters in the story.

Character clues (page 21) is about how authors communicate a character's feelings through recounting what they do and say in detail, using powerful verbs, adjectives and adverbs. Focus on the techniques in order to help the children to explore how authors write: the use of description (expressive adjectives, comparatives and superlatives such as *wider and wider*, also powerful verbs and precise nouns: *A frown creased his brow*).

Feelings thermometers (page 22) helps the children to identify and record how a character feels at specific points in a story. They could also explain what made the character feel like this and how the author communicated it, giving examples.

Stories from other cultures

These activities help the children to notice the features of the cultures of the stories they read, to compare these with their own environment and to be aware of the ways in which the setting affects the characters and the story.

See the setting (page 23) helps the children to focus on the details that authors include in order to communicate to the reader what a setting is like in a way that helps them to imagine the setting using the senses. Focus on the techniques in order to help the children to explore how authors write: for example, powerful verbs (*pecking and bobbing*), precise nouns (*menace*), verbs enhanced by adverbs (*crept threateningly, dozing comfortably*) and adjectives (*friendly, tumbledown*). Encourage the children to remember the key points about each

part of the setting: a small farmhouse with a barn, tumbledown outbuildings and a dusty farmyard with chickens pecking around; a remote mountainside setting. Ask them to identify the words and phrases that communicate the atmosphere and suggest what might happen. They should notice an atmosphere that changes from peaceful to menacing.

Research a setting and **A different culture** (pages 24–25) provide formats to raise the children's awareness of the key features of a setting in a culture different from their own and help them to record their observations and to compare another culture with their own. It is important to discuss ideas such as customs and unfamiliar settings because it can be difficult for children to isolate aspects of their own lifestyle and culture. Encourage them to notice what the author reveals about the setting and culture in the story and then to use other sources to find out more. Also encourage them to consider how people, in real life and in stories, are affected by the culture around them. They could develop stories of their own by researching a setting, placing a character from another story in it and considering what might happen and how the character would respond. This could be linked with sentence structure work on dialects and non-standard English, also with work in citizenship (Living in a diverse world).

Stories that raise issues or dilemmas

In these activities the children consider important issues that occur in stories or dilemmas characters have to face. They have opportunities to identify the choices characters make and to deduce the reasons for their choices of courses of action. You could link these with work in citizenship on Choices. The activities offer opportunities to discuss why authors write about these issues: for example, their importance to the author (and why they are important to him or her – the children could research this using the Internet).

Consequences (page 26) focuses on the actions of a story character. The children identify the key actions taken by the character and the consequences of these actions. They also consider what might have happened if the character had made a different choice and how it would have affected the story.

What's the issue? 1 and **2** (pages 27–28) present a passage from a story that features bullying. The children are asked to consider the main character's point of view as well as those of the victim, the bully and the teacher. They make notes about the choices the characters could make and the possible outcomes. The main character's name does not appear. His name is Michael, but the children should notice that the story is written in the first person, through his eyes and so he is referred to here as *I* or *me* and the pronouns *we, our*, etc. are used.

Dear diary (page 29) provides a diary format in which the children can record a story character's experiences and responses to those experiences. You could change Day 1, Day 2, etc. to Week 1, Week 2, etc. if that is more appropriate. The children could also use this format for making notes about a story they are writing about a character who faces a dilemma or issue; this will help them to explore the significance of the issue, how the character's choice affects himself/herself and other characters and the subsequent events of the story.

Letter to a character (page 30) provides an opportunity for the children to write (possibly in role) to advise a story character what to do in the face of a dilemma, and why. They could first give advice through role-play and hot-seating activities. You could stop reading a story with them at the point where the character faces the dilemma and then, after they have considered the issue and written their letters, continue reading the story to find out what choice the character made.

Turning point (page 31) helps the children to focus on an important scene in a story. You could choose the scene or, for a more challenging activity, ask the children to choose an important scene. Encourage them to look for evidence in the text that shows the character's point of view and possible actions. The children could compare and discuss their ideas, using evidence from the story to support them. You could use this activity to provide opportunities for role-play and contexts for drama.

Plays

These activities develop the children's understanding of the characteristics of play scripts. The activities are sequenced in a way that helps the children to appreciate how a story is presented in a script: how the author communicates the setting, characters, actions and dialogue.

Story to script: the story (page 32) helps the children to identify the features of the story that need to be considered when writing a play script: setting, characters, dialogue and action.

Story to script: production (page 33) focuses on recreating a story setting and characters on stage. The children prepare notes for scenery, props, casting, costume and make-up.

Story to script: the script (page 34) is about dialogue and stage directions. The children should reread the passage and consider how the script can tell the actors what to say, how to say it and what to do.

Book and screen (page 35) is about comparing a book with its screen version. Ask the children to compare what they can find out about the setting, atmosphere and characters of a story from a film and from a book. Also compare how we find out about the events from a book and from a film, what readers see, hear or are told and what they have to imagine. The focus is on how each medium communicates to the audience: the setting and its atmosphere (sounds, what can be seen, smells, feelings and so on), the characters (including age, appearance, thoughts and feelings) and actions (including how they are carried out).

Non-fiction
Recounts: newspapers and magazines

This section focuses on the features of non-fiction recounts, including the sequence of events, details of where they took place and the people involved, and the distinction between fact and opinion.

Much ado (page 36) introduces the main points that should be included in a news recount: what happened, who did it, when and where. The children identify and make notes about these. They could also collect recounts that interest them from local or national newspapers and summarise the main points to present to the class in a 'news round'. You could also draw the children's attention to the features of newspaper recounts: the purpose and characteristics of a headline (including style: rhyme, alliteration and play on words to attract readers' attention), sub-headings and byline. Page 39 focuses on headlines in more detail.

That's a fact (page 37) is about distinguishing between fact and opinion and developing an awareness of the way in which an opinion is sometimes communicated through the choice of words used in presenting facts. As a supplementary extension activity the children could rewrite the recount to make Burger Bite sound attractive. Draw out that the new recount tells the same story and facts but presents them differently.

Just give me the facts (page 38) develops the children's skills in identifying facts and opinions and rewriting sentences to give facts without any opinion. They could first read the sentences with a partner and underline in different colours the words that communicate facts and opinions. During the plenary session you could discuss the effect the choice of words has on readers: it could influence their opinions.

Headline match (page 39) focuses on the purpose of a headline: to provide a brief indication of what a story is about in a way which attracts readers. You could also cut out recounts from newspapers and cut off the headlines: the children could match the headlines to the recounts or write their own headlines.

Match report (page 40)  prepares the children for using what they have learned about newspaper recounts to help them to structure their own recount. They place the events from the reporter's jumbled notes in chronological order along a time-line. Also provide some football match recounts from newspapers for the children to read. They could list the main events on a time-line: draw out that the writer might not begin the recount with the first event, but open with something to engage the readers' attention.

Information texts

These activities develop the children's skills in preparing for research, locating and collecting information and making notes.

What Nooria knows (page 41) is about reviewing what is already known, identifying what to find out and knowing where to look for this information. The activity encourages the children to develop a hypothesis and to identify and summarise evidence to support it. They should read Nooria's 'thought bubbles' about what she knows and suggest what else she could find out and where to find it. Useful sources might include books, CD-ROMs, websites, films and television documentaries. The children could use a blank copy of this page to carry out the same process when preparing for research in other subjects. Ask them what they know about the topic and to express their opinions of life at the time (for example, *Evacuation was a sad time for children* or *evacuation must have been exciting*) and to use sources such as books, CD-ROMs or the Internet to find facts to support their ideas.

Call my bluff: 1 and **2** (pages 42–43) provide practice in using dictionaries to check the definitions of the words on the cards. The children use the organisational features of a dictionary to find information effectively. Before they do so, encourage them to use analogy and what they know about word roots to help them to deduce the correct definitions. Alternatively, the children could use the cards to play their own version of 'Call my bluff' in groups of six. Points could be scored for correct guesses. Encourage them to make up their own definition cards.

Holes, hollows and hideouts
(page 44) develops skills in making and organising brief notes. The children could make a prediction about what makes a habitat suitable for an animal and then use evidence from texts to support this.

They could then write a report about the habitats of mythical animals using their notes and without looking at the report presented in the texts on this page.

Text types: 1 and **2** (pages 45–46) provide a recount, a report and an explanation text. The children classify the texts according to the features they notice: person, tense and connectives. They could also look at sentence type and the verb forms in these sentences.

An explanation (page 47) provides an example explanation of a process. It can be used for showing the children the features of an explanation: heading, introduction, stage-by-stage explanation with each stage building on the previous one, labelled diagrams, logical connectives and a summary. (The summary is the last paragraph, which begins *So the user has to…*) The children could make a prediction about how a yoyo works and then use evidence from the text on this page to support this.

Explanation expert (page 48) provides an incomplete explanation of a process for the children to complete, using what they learned from page 47. If the children explain that the holes are round to fit the shape of the pencil, ask them to look inside it. They should notice the conical shape that makes the blade shave the pencil into a point.

That's why (page 49) develops the children's understanding of the structure of an explanation of a decision based on facts. They are asked to present the facts as an explanation as to why Ian cannot have a dog.

Persuasive texts

This section develops skills in identifying how language can be used in order to persuade people to do something through appealing to their feelings.

Buy now! (page 50) is about how advertisements appeal to readers through their choice of adjectives and the use of memorable combinations of words created by rhyme, alliteration, jingles and serious scientific language. In order to draw attention to the emotional appeal of the interesting language used and the rational appeal of serious scientific language you could ask the children to compare and contrast the two types of language used.

The persuaders (page 51) provides a format on which the children can record their observations about advertisements for trainers. They need access to printed, television, radio and Internet

advertisements. During the plenary session volunteers could use their notes to help them to present their observations to the class.

The language of advertising (page 52) focuses on the style of language used in different advertisements by considering the type of sentence used: instruction, exclamation and question. Ask the children to keep notes of examples of these so that they can explain how they appeal to the audience.

Persuasive feelings: 1 and **2** (pages 53–54) develop the children's awareness of how advertisements appeal to the emotions of their audience. They could use what they have learned to help them to identify how other advertisements they come across appeal to their audience – and who is the audience.

Poetry
Creating images

> Here the children read and respond to poems that contain similes to create a vivid picture for the reader. They also have opportunities to explore and create similes and to enjoy their effects.

Similes kit: beginnings and **Similes kit: endings** (pages 55–56) encourage the children to enjoy the effect of similes as they match the beginnings and endings or write their own beginnings or endings. Point out that some beginnings will have more than one plausible ending: for example, *lips as thin as twigs/flattened worms*. The children should think about which is more graphic, or write a different one if they prefer. Ask them about the pictures the similes create in their minds and provide some standard similes, considered by most writers to be clichés, with which they can compare these: for example, *as right as rain, as hard as iron, as cold as ice, as heavy as lead, as cool as a cucumber, as green as grass, as happy as the day is long.*

Simile poem: 1 and **2** (pages 57–58) encourage the children to explore the similes created by Eve Merriam, an American poet. First let them enjoy the poem, then ask them to talk to a partner about the picture each simile conjures up for them. Point out that, instead of using clichés, this poem uses similes in an original way to produce vivid images of two different trees. Ask the children to imagine each tree and where it grows. They could compare their drawings with images of willows and ginkgos in information books or on websites about trees. They should then try writing their own tree poems, creating different effects through different similes. Discuss various types of trees, and help the children to pick pairs of trees of contrasting appearance: for example, fir or pine and horse chestnut, oak and silver birch.

The right word (page 59) develops the children's appreciation of the connotations of words by trying different words in their place and comparing the different effects. The children could list possible verbs before they choose some to complete each sentence in the most effective way. Also ask them to write two

descriptions of someone (for example, a story character): one that makes the person sound attractive and one that makes him or her sound repulsive.

Gentle phrases, powerful phrases (page 60) focuses on the sounds of phrases and develops the children's appreciation of how the choice of words in a poem can create a vivid picture for the reader. Here the effects considered are gentle or powerful: the children could also consider others: energetic/calm, slow/fast and so on. Use the following as examples:

Gentle
nestled in his resting place (*Midnight*, Thomas Sackville)
silvery arches (*The Whale*, Erasmus Darwin)
sweet airs (*The Tempest*, William Shakespeare)

Powerful
a roaring in the wind (*Morning After a Storm*, William Shakespeare)
burning bright (*The Tyger*, William Blake)
fearful symmetry (*The Tyger*, William Blake)
clasps the crag (*The Eagle*, Alfred, Lord Tennyson)
like a thunderbolt (*The Eagle*, Alfred, Lord Tennyson)

Exploring form

> This section focuses on poetic form: arrangement of lines, number of lines, length of lines, rhyme pattern and rhythm.

Poems alike: 1, **2** and **3** (pages 61–63) present a series of poems: haiku, prayers, couplets and limericks. Before the children are told the name of each poetic form they look for similarities and differences between them and describe them using the chart to help. Ask them to read the poems aloud first (this could be a group or class reading activity). It is important that they have an opportunity to enjoy the poems before they analyse their forms. Their reading could be recorded so that they can play it back as they complete the chart. Some children might be able to add a column to the chart relating to purpose or 'mood': for example, peaceful, funny, descriptive, thoughtful.

On the wrong lines (page 64) develops the children's appreciation of rhythm and rhyme by replacing a line in each verse of two poems with incorrect lines. Explain that poets sometimes change rhyme schemes for particular effects: for example, ending a poem with a couplet. *Answers:* 'Windy Nights' line 6 should be *Why does he gallop and gallop about?* and line 9 should be *By, on the highway, low and loud;* 'The Mad Gardener's Song' line 6 should be *"The bitterness of Life!"* and line 12 should be *"I'll send for the Police!"*

Using the CD-ROM

The PC CD-ROM included with this book contains an easy-to-use software program that allows you to print out pages from the book, to view them (e.g. on an interactive whiteboard) or to customise the activities to suit the needs of your pupils.

Getting started
It's easy to run the software. Simply insert the CD-ROM into your CD drive and the disk should autorun and launch the interface in your web browser.

If the disk does not autorun, open 'My Computer' and select the CD drive, then open the file 'start.html'.

Please note: this CD-ROM is designed for use on a PC. It will also run on most Apple Macintosh computers in Safari however, due to the differences between Mac and PC fonts, you may experience some unavoidable variations in the typography and page layouts of the activity sheets.

The Menu screen
Four options are available to you from the main menu screen.

The first option takes you to the Activity Sheets screen, where you can choose an activity sheet to edit or print out using Microsoft Word.

(If you do not have the Microsoft Office suite, you might like to consider using OpenOffice instead. This is a multi-platform and multi-lingual office suite, and an 'open-source' project. It is compatible with all other major office suites, and the product is free to download, use and distribute. The homepage for OpenOffice on the Internet is: www.openoffice.org.)

The second option on the main menu screen opens a PDF file of the entire book using Adobe Reader (see below). This format is ideal for printing out copies of the activity sheets or for displaying them, for example on an interactive whiteboard.

The third option allows you to choose a page to edit from a text-only list of the activity sheets, as an alternative to the graphical interface on the Activity Sheets screen.

Adobe Reader is free to download and to use. If it is not already installed on your computer, the fourth link takes you to the download page on the Adobe website.

You can also navigate directly to any of the three screens at any time by using the tabs at the top.

The Activity Sheets screen
This screen shows thumbnails of all the activity sheets in the book. Rolling the mouse over a thumbnail highlights the page number and also brings up a preview image of the page.

Click on the thumbnail to open a version of the page in Microsoft Word (or an equivalent software program, see above.) The full range of editing tools are available to you here to customise the page to suit the needs of your particular pupils. You can print out copies of the page or save a copy of your edited version onto your computer.

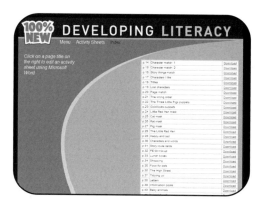

The Index screen
This is a text-only version of the Activity Sheets screen described above. Choose an activity sheet and click on the 'download' link to open a version of the page in Microsoft Word to edit or print out.

Technical support
If you have any questions regarding the *100% New Developing Literacy* or *Developing Mathematics* software, please email us at the address below. We will get back to you as quickly as possible.

educationalsales@acblack.com

In the past

- **Read the opening of *Carrie's War* by Nina Bawden.**
- **What can you work out about the** `characters` **and the** `setting` **(place and time)?**
- **Underline the words and phrases that give clues.**

Carrie had often dreamed about coming back. In her dreams she was twelve years old again; short, scratched legs in red socks and scuffed, brown sandals, walking along the narrow, dirt path at the side of the railway line to where it plunged down, off the high ridge, through the Druid's Grove. The yew trees in the Grove were dark green and so old that they had grown twisted and lumpy, like arthritic fingers. And in Carrie's dream, the fingers reached out for her, plucking at her hair and her skirt as she ran. She was always running by the end of this dream, running away from the house, uphill towards the railway line.

But when she did come back, with her own children, the railway line had been closed. The sleepers had been taken up and the flat, stony top of the ridge was so overgrown with blackberries and wild rose and hazelnut bushes that it was like pushing through a forgotten forest in a fairy tale. The tangled wood round Sleeping Beauty's castle. Pulling off the sticky brambles that clung to their jeans, Carrie's children said, 'No one's been here for hundreds of years...'

'Not hundreds, *thousands*...'

'A hundred, thousand years. A million, billion, trillion...'

'Only about thirty,' Carrie said. She spoke as if this was no time at all. '*I* was here, with Uncle Nick, thirty years ago. During the war – when England was at war with Germany. The Government sent the children out of the cities so they shouldn't be bombed. We weren't told where we were going. Just told to turn up at our schools with a packed lunch and a change of clothes, then we went to the station with our teachers. There were whole train-loads of children sent away like that...'

NOW TRY THIS!

- **Make notes about the characters and the setting.**

Think about approximate age, family and experiences.

Think about historical events.

Teachers' note Ask the children to read the passage with a partner. Ask them when they think the story was set and in what country. How can they tell? Help them to make links with what they have learned in history lessons. Ask them to reread the passage and to look for details that give clues to the setting and to underline them. Draw out that setting means time as well as place.

100% New Developing Literacy
Understanding and Responding
to Texts: Ages 8–9
© A & C BLACK

A historical setting

- **Underline the key words and phrases that show how Flavia Gemina's home is different from modern ones.**
- **Look up any new words and write their meanings on a separate sheet of paper.**

Use a dictionary.

Flavia Gemina solved her first mystery on the Ides of June in the tenth year of the Emperor Vespasian.

She had always had a knack for finding things her father misplaced: his best toga, his quill pen, and once even his ceremonial dagger. But this time there had been a real crime, with a real culprit.

It was a hot, still afternoon, for the sea breeze had not yet risen. Flavia had just settled herself in the garden by the fountain, with a cup of peach juice and her favourite scroll.

'Flavia? Flavia!' Her father's voice came from the study. Flavia took a sip of juice and quickly scanned the scroll to find her place. She would just read one or two lines. After all, the study was so close, just the other side of the fig tree. Her house – like many others in the Roman port of Ostia – had a secret garden at its centre, invisible to anyone on the street. From that inner garden it was only a few steps to the dining room, the kitchen, the store-room, a small latrine, and the study.

* * *

The study had two doors. One small folding door led into the atrium at the front of the house. On the opposite wall a wide doorway opened directly out onto the inner garden. This could be closed off with a heavy curtain.

Now this curtain was pulled right back, and sunlight from the garden fell directly onto the desk, lighting up the sheets of parchment so that they seemed to glow. A little inkpot blazed silver in the sunshine. It was fixed onto the desk so that it would not go missing. For the same reason, the silver quill pen was attached to the desk by a silver chain.

From *The Thieves of Ostia* by Caroline Lawrence

NOW TRY THIS!

- **Where and when in history is the story set?**
- **Write how you can tell.**

Teachers' note Ask the children to skim the passage and to say where and when it was set. They can then read the passage in detail with a partner and think about how this setting is different from the one they live in. During the plenary session you could discuss how the setting affects the story. Could the events have happened in a modern setting? What would be different?

100% New Developing Literacy
Understanding and Responding
to Texts: Ages 8–9
© A & C BLACK

Past talk

- **Underline the expressions we no longer use.**
- **Rewrite them in** modern English.

Use the surrounding text to work out their meanings.

'So I've caught you at last, have I, you young thief?' said the Station Master.

'I'm not a thief,' said Peter, as firmly as he could. 'I'm a coal-miner.'

'Tell that to the Marines,' said the Station Master.

'It would be just as true whoever I told it to,' said Peter.

'You're right there,' said the man, who held him. 'Stow your jaw, you young rip, and come along to the station.'

'I didn't think it was stealing. I thought if I took it from the outside of the heap, perhaps it would be. But in the middle I thought I could fairly count it only mining. It'll take thousands of years for you to burn up all that coal and get to the middle.'

'Not quite. But did you do it for a lark or what?'

'Not much lark carting that beastly heavy stuff up the hill,' said Peter, indignantly.

'Then why did you?' The Station Master's voice was so much kinder now that Peter replied: 'You know that wet day? Well, Mother said we were too poor to have a fire. We always had fires when it was cold at our other house, and …'

'Well,' said the Station Master, rubbing his chin thoughtfully, 'I'll look over it this once. But you remember, young gentleman, stealing is stealing, and what's mine isn't yours, whether you call it mining or whether you don't. Run along home.'

'Do you mean you aren't going to do anything to us? Well, you are a brick,' said Peter, with enthusiasm.

From *The Railway Children* by E. Nesbit

Tell that to the Marines
I can't believe that!

Teachers' note Tell the children that this passage from a story set in the past contains dialogue that includes words and phrases we no longer use. Ask them to read the passage and to discuss it in pairs to work out what these expressions mean.

Historical clues

- **Look for** `historical` **clues in a story.**

Story title _____

Author _____

Record them on the chart.

Real historical characters	_____
Streets and buildings	_____
Objects that are no longer used or that have changed	_____
Language	_____
Lifestyle: food clothes leisure work shopping	_____

NOW TRY THIS!

How would the story change?

- **Could this story have happened in modern times? Why? Why not?**
- **Talk to a partner and make notes.**

Teachers' note Use this page as a format to help the children to record clues about the setting of any story set in the past (for suggested texts, see the list on page 6). Ask them when they first realised that the story was set in the past, when they realised exactly when and where it was set and what they know about that period from their work in history.

100% New Developing Literacy Understanding and Responding to Texts: Ages 8–9
© A & C BLACK

Look and listen

- **Watch a television** drama **set in the past.**
- **What clues told you it was set in the past?**

Title _____

Author _____

Look at the details. Listen.

👁 **What I saw**	🔊 **What I heard**
Scenery _____ _____ _____	Music _____ _____ _____
Props _____ _____ _____	Spoken words _____ _____ _____
Costumes _____ _____ _____	_____ _____
Behaviour _____ _____ _____ _____	How characters spoke _____ _____ _____ _____

NOW TRY THIS!

- **What different clues about the past does the audience get:**
  - **from a book?**
  - **from a television drama?**

Teachers' note Use this page to help the children to record what they notice about a television drama set in the past. It is important first to let them enjoy the drama and to talk about the story in an informal way. They could make notes from memory and then replay the programme in order to look for details.

**100% New Developing Literacy
Understanding and Responding
to Texts: Ages 8–9**
© A & C BLACK

17

The world of Harry Potter

- Make notes about how Harry Potter's world is different from your own.
- Add to the chart as you read each book in the series.

Titles: Harry Potter and the …

About Harry Potter's world	Philosopher's Stone	Chamber of Secrets	Prisoner of Azkaban	Goblet of Fire	Order of the Phoenix	Half-Blood Prince	Deathly Hallows
Transport							
Food							
Money							
School							
Communication							
Other							

18

Teachers' note If possible, enlarge this page to A3. Ask the children about any Harry Potter books they have read. How is his world different from theirs? Different groups could read (or reread) different books from the series and make notes about what they learned about Harry Potter's world in each book.

100% New Developing Literacy
Understanding and Responding
to Texts: Ages 8–9
© A & C BLACK

Atmospheric

- **Describe the** | atmosphere | **of each** | setting | **.**
- **Write notes about what action might happen there.**

Setting	Atmosphere	Action
The ruddy brick floor smiled up at the smoky ceiling; the oaken settles, shiny with long wear, exchanged cheerful glances with each other; plates on the dresser grinned at pots on the shelf, and the merry firelight played over everything.		
Drowsy animals, snug in their holes while wind and rain were battering at their doors, recalled still keen mornings, an hour before sunrise, when the white mist clung closely along the surface of the water; then the shock of the early plunge, the scamper along the bank, and the radiant transformation of earth, air, and water, when the sun was with them again, and grey was gold and colour was born and sprang out of the earth once more.		
The pattering increased till it sounded like sudden hail on the dry-leaf carpet spread around him. The whole wood seemed running now, running hard, hunting, chasing, closing in round something or – somebody? From *The Wind in the Willows* by Kenneth Grahame		

Use the word-bank or other words of your own.

Word-bank

fresh	frightening	happy	homely
jolly	peaceful	scary	threatening
attack	awake	chase	enjoy
escape	explore	run away	sleep

Teachers' note Ask the children if they know the story of *The Wind in the Willows*. Draw out that the main setting is the riverbank and that these are places near the riverbank. During the plenary session discuss the words and phrases that create the atmosphere in each setting. As an extension activity, ask the children to change the words in one passage to give it a different atmosphere.

100% New Developing Literacy **Understanding and Responding to Texts: Ages 8–9** © A & C BLACK

Characters in settings

- **Imagine a │character│ you know in these │settings│.**
- **Write what the character might do.**

Character _____ Author _____

Book title _____

Dark purple and grey clouds frowned down on the gloomy shore. A wave gathered force, sucking shingle from the shore, pulling and gripping, then flung it like machine-gun fire. It rattled across the rocks.

_____

_____

_____

_____

_____

_____

_____

_____

The air was still. A hush hung over the garden, broken only by the humming of a bee. The lilac blossom hung heavily on weary branches, its sweet scent lying on the air.

Sharp blades skimmed the ice. A gang of boys sped past, their arms pumping like pistons and legs a blur. Beginners wobbled, caught one another's arms.

_____

_____

_____

_____

NOW TRY THIS!

- **Change the description of one setting.**
- **How might this affect the character?**

Teachers' note Ask the children if they think the setting of an imaginary world affects what the characters do. They could give examples of characters' actions and then consider how that character might act in these settings, and why. Help them to make links between personal characteristics and qualities and responses to a situation.

100% New Developing Literacy
Understanding and Responding
to Texts: Ages 8–9
© A & C BLACK

Character clues

- **What are these** | characters |
  thinking or feeling?
- **What might they do?**

Write notes.

Leroy opened the box and a smile spread over his face. It stretched wider and wider until it seemed as if it would meet at the back of his head.

_____

_____

Strong gusts of wind swept her words away down the hill and across the valley and her hair streamed behind her.

_____

_____

He looked at the scribbled note for about the tenth time. He read it again – aloud this time. A frown creased his brow. He breathed a long slow breath. Then he turned the paper over, smoothing it carefully. Perhaps if he held it up to the light…

_____

_____

Mr Khan's mouth smiled at us but his eyes shot hard glints through us.

_____

_____

Rani turned pale and stood very still, hardly daring to breathe. Her mouth opened but no words came out.

_____

_____

He took a step forward, placing his right foot carefully, and took a deep breath before lifting his left foot. His knuckles were white as he gripped the rail.

_____

_____

Mrs Steele did not smile. She didn't speak. She didn't move. We waited for what seemed like an hour.

_____

_____

NOW TRY THIS!

- **Choose two of the short passages above.**
- **Write the next two or three sentences.**
- **What might the character be thinking or feeling?**

Teachers' note Ask the children if they can tell how a character feels. Does the author always tell the reader this directly: for example, *He felt miserable, She was worried, He was scared*, or are there other clues (for example, descriptions of what they did, and how, their body language or their facial expression)? Ask the children to look for clues in these passages.

**100% New Developing Literacy
Understanding and responding
to texts: Ages 8–9
© A & C BLACK**

Feelings thermometers

- **Colour the thermometers to show how a character's `feelings` change.**

Book _____

Character _____

Author _____

Chapter(s) _____

happiness

0 1 2 3 4 5

anger

0 1 2 3 4 5

excitement

0 1 2 3 4 5

fear

0 1 2 3 4 5

On the lines, make a note of the setting alongside each thermometer you have coloured in.

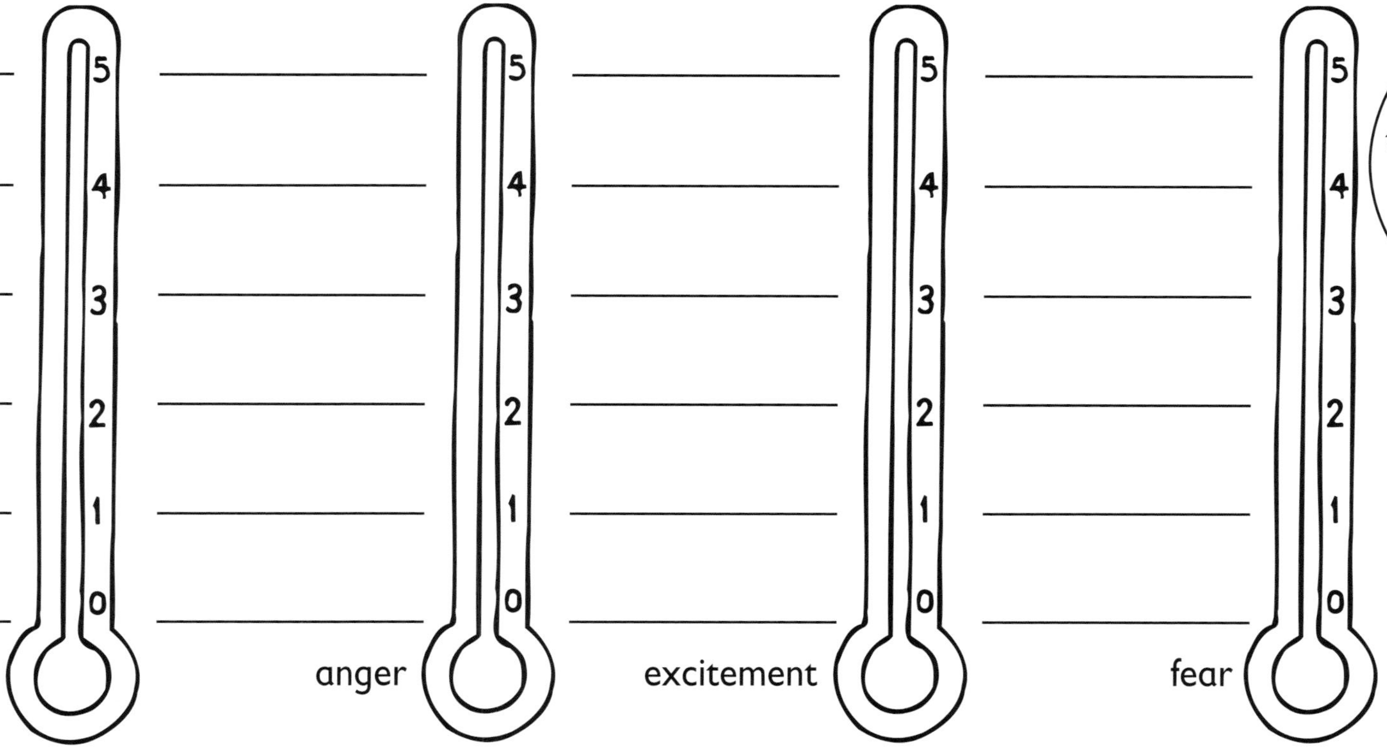

NOW TRY THIS!

- **Choose one thermometer.**
- **Describe how and why the character's feelings change.**

Teachers' note Give the children several copies of this page so they can record a character's feelings in different chapters of a book. See page 6 for examples of books to use. Explain the 0–5 scale on the thermometers: for example, 0 on the 'fear' thermometer is 'not afraid' and 5 is 'terrified'. During the plenary session you could discuss what caused the feelings and what made them change.

100% New Developing Literacy Understanding and Responding to Texts: Ages 8–9 © A & C BLACK

See the setting

- **Underline the words that help you to 'see' this** `setting` **in your mind.**

Look for descriptions.

I would open the back door of the small farmhouse with the bucket of chicken feed in my hand, and the chickens would follow me across the dusty yard and into the barn, pecking and bobbing about while I poured the mixture of grains and grits into the long, low trough by the door.

* * *

We had few neighbours, perched as we were halfway up the mountainside, and Rita's family were the nearest.

* * *

The yard had always seemed a friendly place, the tumbledown sheds that surrounded it dozing comfortably in the heat, but this evening I felt menace in every dark corner as the lengthening shadows of nightfall crept threateningly towards me.

From *On the Run* by Elizabeth Laird

- **Cover the passage.**
- **Describe the setting in your own words.**

_____

_____

_____

_____

_____

NOW TRY THIS!

- **What kind of story might happen in this setting?**
- **Write notes about your ideas.**

Teachers' note Ask the children to read the passage and notice what the setting is like. Without looking at the passage, they could describe it in their own words or even draw pictures of it. They can then focus on the words that helped them to imagine the setting, make notes and write their own description of it.

100% New Developing Literacy Understanding and Responding to Texts: Ages 8–9 © A & C BLACK

Research a setting

- **What can you find out about an unfamiliar** setting :
  - **– from the story?**
  - **– from other sources?**
- **Write your findings on the chart.**

Write notes.

Title _____

Author _____

Setting _____

	Information about the setting	
	from the story	**from information books, CDs and the Internet**
Landscape		
Climate		
Homes		
Clothes		
Food		
Customs		

NOW TRY THIS!

- **How would the main character behave in a different setting?**
- **Write notes about how the story might change.**

Teachers' note Use this page to help the children to record what they find out about a setting in another culture. They can then discuss how the culture and setting affect the characters and the story.

100% New Developing Literacy Understanding and Responding to Texts: Ages 8–9 © A & C BLACK

A different culture

- **Record the differences between the** culture **in a story and your culture.**

Culture means way of life: customs, beliefs, language and so on.

Title _____

Author _____

Setting _____

	Story culture	My culture
Customs		
Beliefs		
Language or dialect		

NOW TRY THIS!

- **How might a character from the story react to your culture?**
- **Write notes for a new chapter.**

Teachers' note Use this page to help the children to make notes about key features of the culture in a story that is different from their own culture. During the plenary session, ask them about similarities as well as differences: for example, people might follow different ways of life but will have much in common, such as family life.

100% New Developing Literacy
Understanding and Responding
to Texts: Ages 8–9
© A & C BLACK

Consequences

Story _____

Author _____

Main character _____

What did the character do?

What happened as a result?

Key action by character

Consequences

What could he or she have done instead?

Action

Consequences

NOW TRY THIS!

- **Explain why the main character acted as he or she did.**
- **Write some evidence from the story.**

Teachers' note Read a story in which a character has to make a decision about an issue. Stop at the point where the character faces a choice and ask the children about the options he or she has. Use this page to help the children to identify the choices and to predict the consequences. They could also plan and write their own stories with different outcomes resulting from different choices.

100% New Developing Literacy
Understanding and Responding
to Texts: Ages 8–9
© A & C BLACK

What's the issue? 1

- **What important** | issue | **can you spot in this story?**

- **Underline the words and phrases that give clues about this issue.**

She came into our classroom in the middle of a Monday afternoon … a kind of smudge of a girl like a crayon drawing that Grubber might walk past and rub into rubbish with his elbow if he felt in the mood for a spot of aggro.

This girl looked as if someone had made quite a good job of her in the first place and then some toe-rag such as Grubber had rubbed her over, leaving her little and tired and pale and a bit dirty with a light turned off somewhere.

*** *** ***

I raised my eyes and saw this deprived-looking kid drooping by Miss's desk as if she'd rather be anywhere else at all in the whole world, even if it meant being dead or something. Miss was smiling at her …

So I decided I'd wander up to that desk to borrow the stapler. Not that I needed the stapler just then but it made a good excuse. We've only got one in the classroom and you have to ask for it ever since Grubber tried to staple one of the mice from the Environment Area to a piece of card.

*** *** ***

On the fourth day Grubber at last registered she was there and went up to where she was doing her work at the side of Miss's desk. Miss was with a group in the far corner of the room.

'What's all this, then?' asked Grubber, in a voice like a Rottweiler with laryngitis.

'How you come gits doin' your rubbish 'ere? You ain't no special right 'ere. Git lost, vomit.'

Now Grubber and me, we've always scrapped … We fought at two, three, four, five, six, seven, eight, then at nine I started to go to aikido. After that he couldn't win any more though that didn't stop him trying. No style, though, no discipline, only size and power. Yeah, Grubber's got that. Power.

And he intended using it. He meant to turf out little Smudge from her safe place by Miss's chair. He fancied doing that. Not that he wanted to be there himself, oh no, the further he was from any teacher the better, but if this new kid wanted to be there that wouldn't do. Grubber couldn't have that.

From The Girl Who Stayed For Half a Week by Gene Kemp

Teachers' note Tell the children that they are going to read a passage from a story that includes an important issue – one commonly faced in schools. Ask them to consider what they might do if they were one of the characters. Different groups could consider it from the point of view of a different character: the main character (whose name is Michael), the girl, Grubber or the teacher.

100% New Developing Literacy Understanding and Responding to Texts: Ages 8–9 © A & C BLACK

What's the issue? 2

- **What might the** | main character | **do next?**
- **What** | choices | **does he have?**
- **What might the** | consequences | **be?**

Write notes in the boxes.

Choices   **Consequences**

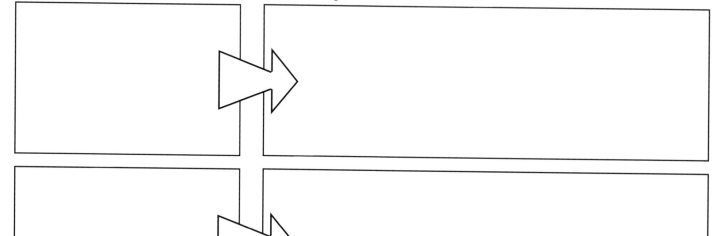

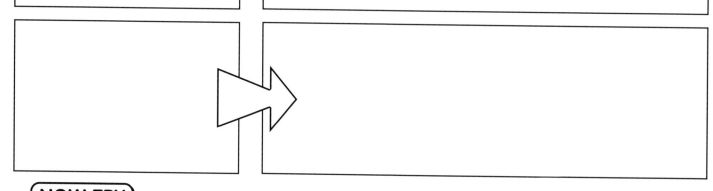

NOW TRY THIS!

- **Predict the events of the story.**
- **Write the next three paragraphs.**

Teachers' note You could use the CD-ROM software to alter this page by masking the 'main character' box and substituting other characters, so that different groups could consider the response of different characters. They could enact the scene to help them to understand the issue.

28

100% New Developing Literacy
Understanding and Responding
to Texts: Ages 8–9
© A & C BLACK

Dear diary

• **Write a diary for the** main character **in a story.**

Use the first person.

Write notes about important events. Write the character's thoughts about a dilemma.

Day 1 _____

_____

_____

Day 2 _____

_____

_____

Day 3 _____

_____

_____

Day 4 _____

_____

_____

Day 5 _____

_____

_____

Day 6 _____

_____

_____

Day 7 _____

_____

_____

Day 8 _____

_____

_____

NOW TRY THIS!

• **What dilemma does the main character face?**
• **Write notes about how it could have been avoided.**

Teachers' note Use this page to help the children to record the main character's (or another character's) responses to events in a story. Emphasise that they should not marely retell the story but record how the character feels and what he or she wants to do and hopes or fears might happen. Remind them to write in the first person.

100% New Developing Literacy
Understanding and Responding
to Texts: Ages 8–9
© A & C BLACK

Letter to a character

- **Write a letter to a character who faces a [dilemma].**
- **Give him or her advice, and say why.**

Show that you understand the situation.

Your address _____

_____

_____

Date _____

Dear _____

I know that _____

_____

You might want to _____

_____

or _____

If you _____

_____

So _____

Yours sincerely

_____

NOW TRY THIS!

- **Write the character's reply to your letter.**

Teachers' note After discussing an issue in which a story character has to make a choice, ask the children to consider what he or she should do and to make notes about the advice they would give before they fill out these notes into a letter. Some children may be able to offer their advice in the role of another character.

100% New Developing Literacy
Understanding and Responding
to Texts: Ages 8–9
© A & C BLACK

Turning point

• **Write a** summary **of an important scene in a story.**

Title _____

Author _____

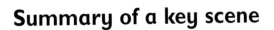

Write notes.

Summary of a key scene

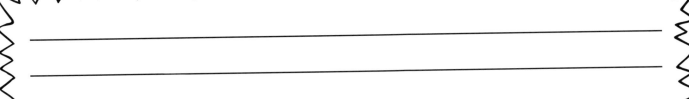

• **Write what the main character is thinking.**

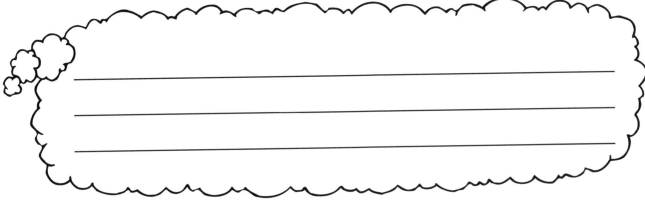

Character's name: _____

NOW TRY THIS!

• **Draw thought bubbles for other characters in this scene.**
• **Write their names and what they are thinking.**

Teachers' note Use this with a shared text. Ask the children to imagine that the story has stopped at a turning point in the events. They can then summarise the main points of the scene and what the main character is thinking in note form. This could be adapted to relate to other characters in the scene.

100% New Developing Literacy
Understanding and Responding
to Texts: Ages 8–9
© A & C BLACK

Story to script: the story

- **Plan a** | play script | **from the passage.**
- **Underline:**

characters' names (in pencil)   spoken words (red)

what characters look like (green)   what characters do (blue)

setting (brown)   props (pink)

The parents of fourteen-year-old Violet, twelve-year-old Klaus and baby Sunny Baudelaire were killed in a fire that burned their house down. Mr Poe found a relative to care for them.

Klaus stepped forward and knocked on Count Olaf's door, his knuckles rapping right in the middle of the carved eye.

There was a pause, and then the door creaked open and the children saw Count Olaf for the first time.

"Hello hello hello," Count Olaf said in a wheezy whisper. He was very tall and very thin, dressed in a grey suit that had many dark stains on it. His face was unshaven, and rather than two eyebrows, like most human beings have, he had just one long one. His eyes were very, very shiny, which made him look both hungry and angry. "Hello, my children. Please step into your new home, and wipe your feet outside so no mud gets indoors."

As they stepped into the house, Mr Poe behind them, the Baudelaire orphans realised what a ridiculous thing Count Olaf had just said. The room in which they found themselves was the dirtiest they had ever seen, and a little bit of mud from outdoors wouldn't have made a bit of difference. Even by the dim light of the one bare lightbulb that hung from the ceiling, the three children could see that everything in this room was filthy, from the stuffed head of a lion which was nailed to the wall to the bowl of apple cores which sat on the small wooden table. Klaus willed himself not to cry as he looked around.

"This room looks like it needs a little work," Mr Poe said, peering around in the gloom.

"I realise that my humble abode isn't as fancy as the Baudelaire mansion," Count Olaf said, "but perhaps with a bit of your money we could fix it up a little nicer." Mr Poe's eyes widened in surprise, and his coughs echoed in the dark room before he spoke. "The Baudelaire fortune," he said sternly, "will not be used for such matters. In fact it will not be used at all until Violet is of age." Count Olaf turned to Mr Poe with a glint in his eye like an angry dog.

From *The Bad Beginning* by Lemony Snicket

Teachers' note Read the introductory paragraph to the story with the children and then ask them to consider how they would turn the passage into a play script. Ask them what they need to find out in addition to what the characters say (how they say it, what they do, what they look like, what the scene looks like, where it is and so on).

100% New Developing Literacy Understanding and Responding to Texts: Ages 8–9 © A & C BLACK

Story to script: production

- **Plan a** `play` **from the passage.**
- **Write on the notepads.**

Who are they?
How old are they?
How are they related?

Characters

_____   _____
_____   _____
_____   _____

Notes for wardrobe and make-up

Character	Clothes	Make-up, wigs and so on

Notes for scenery and props

Scene	Scenery	Props
1. Street outside Count Olaf's house		
2. Main room at Count Olaf's		

Teachers' note Use this with page 32 or after discussing a scene from another story the children have read. Tell them that they are the production assistants on a play and have to make notes to help everyone who works on the production: actors, stage director, props, and wardrobe and make-up directors. They should write in note form.

100% New Developing Literacy
Understanding and Responding
to Texts: Ages 8–9
© A & C BLACK

Story to script: the script

● Write a ⎡play script⎤ **from the passage on page 32.**

Scene 1 The street outside Count Olaf's house

<u>Enter Violet, Klaus and Sunny from stage left. Mr Poe is following them,</u>
<u>coughing.</u>

Mr Poe (<u>between coughs</u>): Here we are – your new home!

Klaus (<u>looking rather nervously up at the tall building</u>): Is this really Count
Olaf's house?

Violet: But it's horrible! Knock on the door, Klaus – perhaps it's nice inside.

_____

_____

_____

_____

_____

_____

_____

_____

_____

_____

_____

_____

_____

_____

Teachers' note Use this with pages 32 and 33 or you could adapt it to use after discussing a scene
from another story the children have read. Ask them to use their notes to help them to write a
script for the play that not only tells the actors what to say, but how to say it, what to do, and
how. The script should also give information about the setting at the start.

100% New Developing Literacy
Understanding and Responding
to Texts: Ages 8–9
© A & C BLACK

Book and screen

Are you told everything? Make notes.

- Think about a book and film of the same story.
- What does the book tell you? How?
- What does the film tell you? How?

Title _____ Author _____

	Book	Film
Setting: what it looks, sounds and feels like		
Atmosphere		
Characters: ages, names, what they look like, think, feel		
Events: what characters do and say		

Teachers' note Use this page to help the children to compare the screen version of a story with the book. Draw attention to the differences in the ways each medium presents the story – what the audience can see and hear and what they imagine for themselves: in a film someone has interpreted the author's description and narrative, rather than the audience doing this for themselves.

100% New Developing Literacy
Understanding and Responding
to Texts: Ages 8–9
© A & C BLACK

35

Much ado

• **Write a** ⌐summary⌐ **of the** ⌐recount⌐ .

THE TRUMPET
Your favourite local paper –
serving Much Snobbery, Upper Whingeing and Highbrow Hill

WRINKLIES RIDE IN
By Ava Larff

Shoppers in the sleepy country town of Much Snobbery are reeling after a motorcycle gang sped into the market square at 8 am on Friday with much revving of engines and clomping of boots. The gang, known as the Wild Grannies, because they are all female and aged over sixty, took up every single parking bay in the square during their three-hour visit.

TERROR

"It was terrible," said Daisy Quivering, 46, a local resident. "There was nowhere left for us to park. I had to walk at least seven metres to the bakery."

"There were about fifty of them, dressed from head to foot in black leather. My children were terrified," added Ian Nimby, 35.

"The air was full of poisonous fumes from their filthy engines. I was afraid to breathe. This is one of the cleanest towns in Britain – or it was until those polluters came," complained Una Watt, 56, from Much Snobbery

Parish Council. "We shall look into this and find a way of putting a stop to it in the future."

WELCOME

Isla Shothem, 108, the town's oldest resident, said she had had 'a nice cup of tea' with two of the Wild Grannies in the Greaseless Spoon Café. "They told me where I could buy a very good motorbike very cheaply and one took me for a ride on her bike. I do hope they come back," she added. "I haven't had such fun for a long time. I'm going to keep in touch with them by email."

What happened _____

_____

Who did it _____

_____

When _____

Where _____

NOW TRY THIS!

• **Why was the event in the news?**
• **Write a paragraph to explain this.**

Teachers' note Ask the children to identify the main events in the recount. They could underline key words. Focus on what happened, who did the actions, when and where.

100% New Developing Literacy
Understanding and Responding
to Texts: Ages 8–9
© A & C BLACK

That's a fact

- Look for facts and opinions in this news recount .

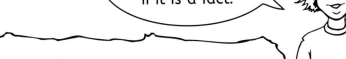
Sometimes an opinion is written as if it is a fact.

BURGER BLIGHT BITES BORINGHAM
By our health correspondent Leticia Goode

BAD DECISION

Town councillors have made a decision that will allow a flashy modern shop-front topped with a model of an ugly giant burger to ruin the High Street – a nasty growth on a lovely Tudor street. Last night they gave Burger Bite planning permission to bring its smelly, greasy, unhealthy food to the heart of this unspoilt village.

HEARTS AT RISK

Heart indeed – the hearts of our youngsters will be at risk when they are tempted by garish posters flinging special offers in their faces: tacky free gifts, double portions of poison and buy-one-get-one-you-don't-need.

HEALTHY VILLAGE SPOILED

Boringham's schools and parents have long prided themselves on their wonderful healthy kitchens, inspired by TV chef Johnny Olive.

"Our children have never seen these disgusting burgers and grease-laden sauces," said Lena Cuisine, 35. "We protect them from these fatty foods filled with salt, sugar and chemicals until they have developed healthy habits and will always make healthy choices."

HEALTH RISK

The village's doctor is bracing himself for an epidemic of obesity, heart attacks and other diseases caused by an unhealthy diet.

Facts	Opinions
_____	_____
_____	_____
_____	_____
_____	_____
_____	_____

NOW TRY THIS!

- **List ten words that communicate that Burger Bite is a bad thing.**

Teachers' note Begin by giving examples of facts (information that can be checked) and opinions (what someone thinks about an object, person, event, place and so on). Point out that opinions are sometimes expressed as if they were facts: for instance, 'The best football team in England is Liverpool' is an opinion, but 'Liverpool won the Premiership this year' is a fact.

100% New Developing Literacy Understanding and Responding to Texts: Ages 8–9 © A & C BLACK

Just give me the facts

- **Rewrite the sentences so that they give only the** facts .

There should be no opinions.

The overgrown wasteland is to be built on.

_____

There will be four superb ultra-modern houses with spacious garages.

_____

_____

She wore a slime green dress and was weighed down by a truckload of jewels.

_____

_____

_____

This charming little cottage has a cosy living room with a homely open fire.

_____

_____

_____

NOW TRY THIS!

- **Rewrite the sentences to give different** opinions .

Teachers' note Read the first example with the children and point out the adjective *overgrown* and the noun *wasteland*. You could replace these with other words such as *grass-covered* and *land*. Discuss the connotations of words such as *overgrown* (suggesting that the area is untidy) and *wasteland* (implying that the land is worthless).

38

100% New Developing Literacy
**Understanding and Responding
to Texts: Ages 8–9**
© A & C BLACK

Headline match

- **Match the** headlines **to the news** reports **.**

Headline	1	2	3	4	5	6	7	8
Report								

1 Double trouble in Year 4 class

2 DAIRY WORKERS CHEESED OFF

3 RIDERS RODE WRONG ROAD

5 CELL HELL

6 Switch in time saves line

4 Onion growers in a pickle

7 All cisterns go for new building

8 CLOCK CLANGER

a The building of ladies' and gents' lavatories on the village green has been approved by planners.

b The region's market gardeners fear that cheap imports of French onions will damage sales.

c Jockeys in the first race at yesterday's meeting mistook the boundary fence for one of the jumps and found themselves riding along the M6. Fortunately there was hardly any traffic because it was

d Identical twins have confused teacher Ava Luke so much that she no longer knows which is which. This makes end of year reports very difficult to write.

e Prisoners at Clink jail have written to the Prime Minister to complain about cramped conditions.

f The low prices paid by supermarkets for dairy products are putting many farmers out of business.

g After complaints from travellers, a new radio-controlled clock has been installed in the station to ensure that trains leave on time.

h There were red faces as the mayor, Councillor Vera M Portant, unveiled the new clock in the shopping mall. It took the audience a few minutes to notice that it had two hour hands.

NOW TRY THIS!

- **Write new headlines for two reports from a newspaper you have seen.**

Use rhyme, alliteration, word-play or humour.

Teachers' note Ask the children to read the first headline and to predict what the newspaper report will be about. They can then look for the one that best matches it. Draw out that headlines should tell the reader very briefly what the report is about so that they are interested in reading it to find out the details.

100% New Developing Literacy
Understanding and Responding
to Texts: Ages 8–9
© A & C BLACK

Match report

Salim dropped his notes about a football match.
Now they are out of order.

- **Read Salim's notes.**
- **Write a very short caption for each picture.**
- **Cut out the pictures and put them in order on a time-line.**

City's 2nd goal – penalty by Green – United's GK (Brown) dived wrong way. Penalty given for foul on City's defender White.

Final score 2-0 for City. Fans sang 'We're going to win the cup'.

Teams announced. Fans cheered.

City's 1st goal – brilliant header by Grey – inside penalty area.

City kicked off. White dribbled past 3 United defenders.

City   United

NOW TRY THIS!

- **Use the notes and time-line to help you to write a match report.**
- **Add an introduction and a summary.**

Teachers' note Use this page to help the children to understand how notes can be filled out to write sentences for a recount about an event. Ask them in which tense the recount should be written. They need an extra sheet of paper on which to draw a time-line.

100% New Developing Literacy Understanding and Responding to Texts: Ages 8–9
© A & C BLACK

What Nooria knows

Nooria is learning about children in the **Second World War.**

- **Read what she knows.**
- **Tell her what else she needs to find out.**
- **Write a list of useful** sources .

She can use books, CD-ROMs and the Internet.

Children from cities were sent away from home. They had a list of things to pack.

Schools were different. Children sat in pairs at wooden desks with inkwells.

Nooria

You could find out _____
_____
_____
_____

Useful sources

Books _____
_____

CD-ROMs _____
_____

Websites _____
_____

Other _____

NOW TRY THIS!

- **Scan the sources to find out which parts will help.**

Teachers' note Use this page to demonstrate how to prepare for research. Ask the children what subject and topic Nooria is going to research. What does she know about this topic? Ask them to use what they have learned from history lessons to suggest what else Nooria could find out. They can then scan books, CD-ROMs and websites and suggest other sources that will help her.

100% New Developing Literacy
Understanding and Responding
to Texts: Ages 8–9
© A & C BLACK

Call my bluff: 1

abode
1. Where someone lives: a home.
2. A type of shellfish.
3. An old word for the past tense of 'obey'.

buckler
1. A manservant in charge of food and drink.
2. A small shield.
3. A shoe fastening.

counterfeit
1. Forged, imitated.
2. A shop assistant.
3. A mathematical problem.

chub
1. A thick layer of fat.
2. A river fish from the trout family.
3. To beat with a thick heavy block of wood.

dormant
1. A mat for wiping your feet on.
2. Someone who guards a doorway.
3. Sleeping or inactive.

frugal
1. Very careful not to use much of anything.
2. A German girl.
3. A fruit pudding.

garret
1. A wire strung across a path as a trap to strangle someone.
2. A bare room in an attic.
3. To drill a hole.

impair
1. To damage or spoil.
2. In groups of two.
3. A rare gas.

jamboree
1. A lively party or celebration.
2. A sweet spread made from fruit.
3. A very boring person.

kale
1. A Lancashire dialect word for coal.
2. A sea fish.
3. A green leafy vegetable similar to cabbage.

Teachers' note Copy the page onto card and cut out the cards. They can be used in several ways: the children could be given a card, predict which meaning is correct, explain why (by analogy with other words or by thinking about the roots of words) and then check their answers using a dictionary. See page 43 for another suggestion.

100% New Developing Literacy Understanding and Responding to Texts: Ages 8–9
© A & C BLACK

Call my bluff: 2

loathe

1. To hate.
2. A type of bread.
3. A machine for cutting wood.

mandolin

1. A language spoken in China.
2. A stringed musical instrument played in a similar way to a guitar.
3. A type of small sweet orange.

notion

1. A cream to be rubbed on the skin for curing aches and pains.
2. An idea.
3. A short letter written on one page.

okra

1. A vegetable.
2. A yellow colour.
3. All right.

parlour

1. To steal.
2. Paleness, especially if someone looks ill.
3. A room for sitting in or entertaining guests.

ration

1. A fixed amount of food allowed in a set time such as a day or week.
2. A young rat.
3. A slice of bacon.

starling

1. A bird about the same size as a blackbird with bluish-black feathers.
2. A small star.
3. Beginning.

tawny

1. Cheap and not well-made.
2. A brown colour.
3. A tall person.

umber

1. An old word meaning 'over' (the opposite to 'under').
2. A brown colour.
3. Offence ('to take umber' = 'to take offence').

wince

1. Meat chopped or ground into small pieces.
2. A shrinking movement made when someone feels pain or distress.
3. A large cash prize.

Teachers' note See page 42. The children could play a bluffing game in two teams of three. One team all have a copy of the same card. They check the true definition, but add their own ideas to make the meanings given sound equally convincing. They then take turns to present these to the other team, who must decide which is correct. The player with the correct definition reveals the answer.

100% New Developing Literacy
Understanding and Responding
to Texts: Ages 8–9
© A & C BLACK

Holes, hollows and hideouts

These children are finding out about the habitats of ⟨mythical⟩ animals.

- **Make notes on the ⟨chart⟩ to compare the habitats.**

> **What have they found out?**

> Unicorns live in dense forests where they can hide from their predators – people. They are magic, so they don't need to eat. The horn takes in food from the sun.

> dragon – lives in caves – esp. near volcanoes (cold-blooded reptile so needs to keep warm) also use lava to help them breathe fire

> Vampires fear light and heat. Live in cold, dark caves away from streams/rivers – can't cross running water.

> Werewolves can take the form of people and live in their home – so that they can eat other people.

Mythical animal	Habitat	What makes the habitat suitable

NOW TRY THIS!

- **Find out about the habitats of other mythical creatures.**
- **Record your findings on a chart.**

> Use books and the Internet.

Teachers' note Ask the children to read the information about habitats and to identify the key facts, which they can record on the chart. They could use this method for research on real animals' habitats or other topics in science. Draw out that a chart is a good way of recording facts because it is quick and the facts are easy to look up later.

100% New Developing Literacy
Understanding and Responding
to Texts: Ages 8–9
© A & C BLACK

Text types: 1

- **Underline the** | verbs |.
- **Underline the** | connectives |.

Use these colours.

Verbs:
present tense – blue
past tense – green

Connectives:
joining (e.g. and, but) – orange
time (e.g. then, next, now) – red
place (e.g. where, including) – pink
reason, purpose or cause (e.g. because, so that) – brown

Boudicca's last battle

In AD60, Boudicca and her horde of 80,000 Britons headed north up Watling Street. The Romans knew they were coming and they waited in a clearing with a wood behind them and open ground in front, where the Britons would come from. Boudicca drove her chariot in front of her people and urged them on. Then the Romans charged forward in a wedge shape, aiming their spears. Soon many Britons lay dead. Now the remaining Britons were hemmed in by their chariots and horses. Nearly every one was killed but only 400 Romans died. During the battle Boudicca escaped, but she died soon afterwards.

Chester

Chester is a typical Roman city. Its name means 'camp' (an army camp) and its streets are in straight lines at right angles to one another. Around the city is a wall the Romans built to defend it. The wall has gateways where the main streets enter the city. Along the wall there are remains of Roman buildings, including part of an amphitheatre.

CHESTER
Roman City

How the hypocaust works

The hypocaust is a type of central heating system. The building has to be made from stone so that it does not catch fire. A furnace is built outside so that the house doesn't become smoky. It has a stoke-hole for fuel and flues to let smoke escape. The stone floors of the building rest on pillars in order to leave a gap to let hot air from the furnace flow through ducts into the rooms above. This happens because hot air rises above the colder air.

Teachers' note Ask the children to identify the passage that tells a story, the one that gives a report about a situation and the one that explains how something works. Remind them of the terms *recount* and *non-chronological report* and introduce the term *explanation*. Ask them to notice the person, tense and form of the verbs and the connectives used. See also page 46.

100% New Developing Literacy Understanding and Responding to Texts: Ages 8–9 © A & C BLACK

Text types: 2

- **What types of text are they?**
- **Fill in the chart.**

Report   Recount   Explanation

Text	Type	Main tense	Colour of most connectives	Person
Boudicca's last battle				
Chester				
How the hypocaust works				

NOW TRY THIS!

- Add three more texts to the chart.
- Tell a friend how you can tell what types they are.

Teachers' note Use this with page 45. Also provide other short texts for the children to read and to notice the features such as person, tense and connectives.

100% New Developing Literacy Understanding and Responding to Texts: Ages 8–9 © A & C BLACK

An explanation

How a yoyo works

The way a yoyo works depends on several different forces acting on it.

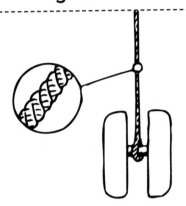

Modern yoyos have a smooth cord so that there is little friction between the cord and the axle of the yoyo.

This cord is wound tightly around the axle. When the user lets go of the yoyo (but keeps hold of the cord) the yoyo can fall downwards.

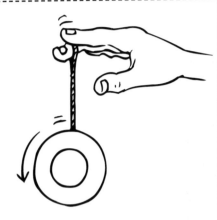

As the yoyo falls it has cord wound around it. The cord lets the yoyo spin as it unwinds.

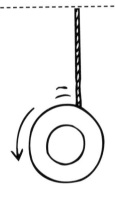

As the yoyo reaches the end of the cord it cannot fall any farther. But it is still spinning in the loop of cord. This spinning keeps the yoyo in place.

The cord eventually starts to rewind. This stops the yoyo spinning. Another force is needed to start it moving back up the string.

So the user has to give a tug on the cord. That is a big enough force to start the yoyo moving upwards. The user catches it and the whole process starts all over again.

Teachers' note Ask volunteers to demonstrate using a yoyo. Ask the children if they know how it works. Encourage them to give verbal explanations as they watch. Present the explanation here and ask them to read it and then, without looking at it, to explain how a yoyo works, focusing on what makes it come back up the cord. Mix up the pictures and ask the children to put them in order.

100% New Developing Literacy Understanding and Responding to Texts: Ages 8–9 © A & C BLACK

Explanation expert

- **Complete this** explanation.
- **Try to make it as clear as possible.**

 What is missing?

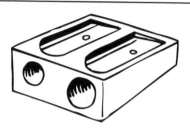

The pencil sharpener has two holes, each with a blade.

_____

_____

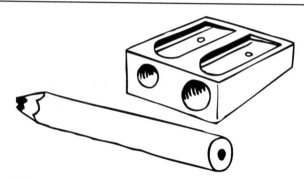

The blunt pencil is put into the hole _____

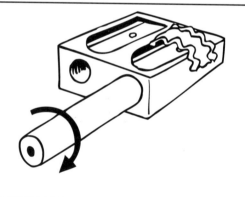

_____

_____

_____

The result is _____

_____

_____

NOW TRY THIS!

- **What is special about the shape of the holes?**
- **Explain why they have this shape.**

48

That's why

There are many reasons why Ian cannot have a dog.

• **Write his mother's** | explanation |.

Write an introduction.
Use connectives.
Write a summary.

Your brother is allergic to animal hair.

There is no-one at home all day.

I'm afraid of dogs.

Our flat is very small.

It is cruel to keep a dog in a small place.

It is not fair to leave it alone all day.

Ian

NOW TRY THIS!

• **Think about something that would be wrong.**
• **Write an explanation to say why it is wrong.**

Teachers' note Use this page to help the children to structure an explanation using the facts provided. If necessary, you could suggest an introduction: for example, *I am afraid we cannot have a dog* or *It would be nice for you to have a dog but there are a lot of reasons why we cannot*. Ask the children to write a summary that repeats this in some way but uses a logical connective such as *so* or *that is why*.

**100% New Developing Literacy
Understanding and Responding
to Texts: Ages 8–9**
© A & C BLACK

Buy now!

- **What language features does the** [advertisement] **use?**
- **Complete the chart.**

Get that tinglesome tang!

One small glass provides one portion of your five a day – contains vitamin C, calcium, magnesium, phosphorus, potassium, beta carotene and folic acid.

Join the punch bunch!

Fresher, tastier, purer, – simply the best!

Full fruit flavour plus vital vitamin C!

Pineapple & Peach

PUNCH 100% pure

As pure as a tropical shower...

Feature	Examples
strong adjectives	
comparatives and superlatives	
made-up words	
alliteration	
rhyme	
similes	
scientific language	
jingles	

NOW TRY THIS!

- **Copy the advertisement format.**
- **Change it to advertise a soup.**

Teachers' note Read the advertisement with the children and ask them to notice the adjectives and language features which are used here and in poetry: rhyme, alliteration and similes. During the plenary session discuss the purpose of each of these: for example, to make the audience remember the product.

50

100% New Developing Literacy Understanding and Responding to Texts: Ages 8–9 © A & C BLACK

The persuaders

- **Look at or listen to** advertisements **for trainers.**

the Internet

radio

television

posters

newspapers, comics and magazines

- **Record how they try to** persuade **you to buy.**

Example of feature

Brand	A famous person wearing them	Limited supplies	Reduced price	Free gift	Special offer for a short time	Latest style – don't be out of date

- **Explain how an advertisement has made you want something.**

Teachers' note Ask the children to read and discuss a collection of advertisements from different media and to look for the features listed on the chart. During the plenary session discuss the purpose of these features: for example, to make readers think they will be like a famous person if they buy the product.

100% New Developing Literacy
Understanding and Responding
to Texts: Ages 8–9
© A & C BLACK

The language of advertising

- **Listen to some** advertisements :
  - **on television**
  - **on the radio.**
- **Count the number of each type of sentence.**

Don't wait.
Get your free gift!
Don't miss this
chance.

Superb!
What a bargain!
Fantastic!

Do you want
to be a loser?
Can you afford
to miss this?

Instruction

Exclamation

Question

Type of goods	Brand	Type of sentence					
		Instruction		Exclamation		Question	
		Tally	Number	Tally	Number	Tally	Number

NOW TRY THIS!

- **What conclusion can you draw from your results?**
- **Discuss this with others and write your ideas.**

Teachers' note Ask the children to listen to a collection of advertisements from different broadcast media and ask them what kind of sentence each one contains: instruction/command, question or exclamation. Explain that the chart helps them to record the results of a survey of these advertisements to find out what types of sentence are used most often.

100% New Developing Literacy Understanding and Responding to Texts: Ages 8–9
© A & C BLACK

Persuasive feelings: 1

(1)

Buy Barkers' biscuits.

Why park in Ipswich?

No, no, no. BARKERS' BISCUITS!

Whose fish tank?

Never mind. Just get some biscuits. The ones with the big yellow B.

(2) Everyone has the right to clean water. Mata has to walk two kilometres to collect a bucket of water. She does this up to five times a day. When she reaches the water hole it is sometimes just a muddy puddle, with animals drinking from it. She and her family risk disease, but it is the only water they have. Any small amount you can give will help us to dig wells that will provide fresh water for people like Mata.

(3)
Look at her feet!
They moved too fast to see!
Cool – what's she wearing?
Super wheelies!
There she goes!

(4) Try our test.
Look at the picture.
What do you see?
If you saw a race horse you are one of those special people with super vision.
Show off your skill. Amaze your friends with our new book of super vision pictures.

(5) *In the box is something we have been developing for more than a year. We decided not to put it on the market until it was absolutely right. We believe in perfection. Watch as we unwrap it layer by layer.*

(6) *Crunch! Mmmmm! Another spoonful! And another! The crispest toffee shell. The creamiest chocolate. The smoothest caramel sauce.*

(7) A burglar could be watching your house now, watching to see who lives there, at what times they go out, how they lock up. A burglar could be looking for the weak spots – and he will find them. With Supersecurity you can be safe. We monitor your home 24 hours a day, giving you peace of mind.

(8)

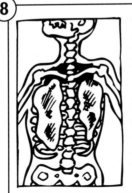

This picture shows Tom's lungs. He has not long to live. He smoked from the age of twelve until he found that he had lung cancer at 52. If he had not smoked he might have lived until he was 72, 82 or even 92.

Teachers' note Ask the children to read the advertising features and to discuss them with a friend for comparison. They can record their responses on the chart on page 54.

100% New Developing Literacy
Understanding and Responding
to Texts: Ages 8–9
© A & C BLACK

Persuasive feelings: 2

- **How do the** | persuasive | **texts make you** | feel |**?**

afraid	amused	clever	curious
excited	frightened	interested	hungry
nervous	pitying	sad	scared
shocked	sorry	special	worried

- **Describe how the texts evoke these feelings.**

Text	Feelings	How it evokes these feelings
1		
2		
3		
4		
5		
6		
7		
8		

NOW TRY THIS!

- **Write a paragraph to persuade your parents to buy something you want.**

Work with a friend.

Teachers' note Ask the children to read the advertising features on page 53 and to discuss them with a friend for comparison. They can record their responses on this chart. During the plenary session, discuss why advertisers try to evoke these feelings and how effective this is in persuasion.

**100% New Developing Literacy
Understanding and Responding
to Texts: Ages 8–9**
© A & C BLACK

Similes kit: beginnings

a man as tall as	a face as round as
hands as wide as	lips as thin as
a jumper as yellow as	a face as red as
cheeks as brown as	a pillow as soft as
fingers as knobbly as	a touch as gentle as
a face as kind as	eyes as black as
a friend as loyal as	hair as spiky as
a dancer as graceful as	a voice as sweet as
a smell as fresh as	a voice as rough as

Teachers' note Copy the cards onto coloured paper or card (use a different colour for the cards on page 56). The children could match the beginnings with the endings on page 56 or they could write their own endings.

100% New Developing Literacy
Understanding and Responding
to Texts: Ages 8–9
© A & C BLACK

Similes kit: endings

a tower	a station clock
fans	flattened worms
a field of sunflowers	ketchup
polished wood	a cloud
twigs	a butterfly's wings
an angel's smile	deep pools
a spaniel	a hedgehog
a flower in the breeze	burnished silk
a garden after the rain	a gravel path

100% New Developing Literacy
Understanding and Responding
to Texts: Ages 8–9
© A & C BLACK

Simile poem: 1

- **What do the** `similes` **make you imagine?**
- **Draw and write in the boxes.**

Willow and Ginkgo

The willow is like an etching,
Fine-lined against the sky.
The ginkgo is like a crude sketch,
Hardly worthy to be signed.
The willow's music is like a soprano,
Delicate and thin.
The ginkgo's tune is like a chorus
With everyone joining in.

The willow is sleek as a velvet-nosed calf;
The ginkgo is leathery as an old bull.
The willow's branches are like silken thread;
The ginkgo's like stubby rough wool.

The willow is like a nymph with streaming hair;
Wherever it grows, there is green and gold and fair.
The willow dips to the water,
Protected and precious, like the king's favorite daughter.

The ginkgo forces its way through gray concrete;
Like a city child, it grows up in the street.
Thrust against the metal sky,
Somehow it survives and even thrives.
My eyes feast upon the willow,
But my heart goes to the ginkgo.

Eve Merriam

Willow

_____

_____

_____

_____

Ginkgo

_____

_____

_____

_____

NOW TRY THIS!

- **Write some similes to make a tree sound** `tall` , `old` , `green` .

Teachers' note Show the children a list of traditional similes (see *Notes on the activities*, page 11) and ask them if they think these help them to picture objects, people or places. Introduce and explain the term *cliché* and point out that these are often used because it is easier to use a cliché than to think up an original description. Then let them read and respond to this poem.

100% New Developing Literacy
Understanding and Responding
to Texts: Ages 8–9
© A & C BLACK

Simile poem: 2

- **Choose two different trees.**
- **What are the shapes of the trees? Where do they grow?**
- **What else do you know about the trees?**
- **Draw the two trees then write your own** | simile poem | **about them.**

_____ **and** _____

The _____ is like _____

The _____ is like _____

_____

_____

_____

_____

_____

_____

_____

_____

_____

_____

_____

_____

_____

Teachers' note Ask the children what they have learned about clichés and original similes and encourage them to think up some of their own to describe two different trees. Suggest they start by drawing the two trees they have chosen and then write their simile poem using images the trees conjure up in their minds.

100% New Developing Literacy
Understanding and Responding
to Texts: Ages 8–9
© A & C BLACK

The right word

• **Change the underlined words to make different** `descriptions` .

Think about the effects of the words.

What do they make you see, hear, smell, taste or feel?

The forest <u>drips</u> and <u>glows</u> with green.

Her jewels _____ and _____ with green.

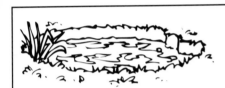
The pond _____ and _____ with green.

His eyes <u>bulged</u> in a <u>blazing</u> glare.

His _____ _____ in a _____ _____.

His _____ _____ in a _____ _____.

NOW TRY THIS!

• **Write a sentence to describe a house.**
• **Change some of the words to make it seem** `homely` , `haunted` , `elegant` **or** `scruffy` .

Teachers' note Ask the children to read the first example and ask them what type of word is underlined (verb). Ask them what makes these verbs expressive – what they make them picture in their minds as they read. Challenge them to think of other expressive/strong verbs to use instead to create a different impression.

100% New Developing Literacy Understanding and Responding to Texts: Ages 8–9
© A & C BLACK

Gentle phrases, powerful phrases

• **Sort the phrases:**

gentle **or** powerful

Read them aloud. Listen to their sounds.

softly splashing

rosy glow

silently sinking

mighty master

glaring giant

slamming and crashing

chirping and chattering

roaring and rushing

striding over fields

skipping among daisies

fluffy feathers

falling flakes

grabbing a gauntlet

sad, soulful eyes

glowering gaze

rock-like grip

Gentle phrases

Powerful phrases

NOW TRY THIS!

• **List other gentle and powerful phrases.**
• **Write some sentences that sound gentle or powerful.**

Teachers' note Ask the children to think about the sounds of the phrases as they read them aloud: gentle or powerful. During the plenary session invite feedback and discuss which combinations of phonemes produce gentle sounds or powerful sounds. Also ask them to think about the effects of long and short vowels.

100% New Developing Literacy Understanding and Responding to Texts: Ages 8–9
© A & C BLACK

Poems alike: 1

- ## Sort the poems into sets with similarities.

Work in a group. Different groups might find different ways of doing this.

① Leisure

What is this life if, full of care,
We have no time to stand and stare.
No time to stand beneath the boughs
And stare as long as sheep or cows.
No time to see, when woods we pass,
Where squirrels hide their nuts in grass.
No time to see, in broad daylight,
Streams full of stars, like skies at night.
No time to turn at Beauty's glance,
And watch her feet, how they can dance.
No time to wait till her mouth can
Enrich that smile her eyes began.
A poor life this if, full of care,
We have no time to stand and stare.

W. H. Davies

② The Old Man of Peru

There was an old man of Peru,
Who dreamt he was eating his shoe.
   He woke in the night
   In a terrible fright,
And found it was perfectly true.

Anon

③ The Young Lady of Russia

There was a Young Lady of Russia
Who screamed so loud no one could hush her;
   Her screams were extreme, –
   No one heard such a scream
As was screamed by that Lady of Russia.

Edward Lear

④ Acorn

Just a green olive
In its own little egg-cup:
It can feed the sky.

Kit Wright

⑤ The young man from Brazil

There was a young man from Brazil
Who cut down the trees on a hill.
   It rained all one day
   And the soil washed away
So life on the hill is now nil.

Colin Nicholls

⑥ Icicle

drip by drip
the moonlight lengthens
in the icicle

David Cobb

⑦ *from* Thanksgiving

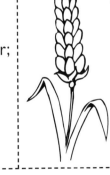

Thank You
   for all my hands can hold –
     and melons gold,
      yellow corn
       both ripe and sweet,
     peas and beans
      so good to eat!

Ivy O. Eastwick

Teachers' note You could display these poems and those on page 62 on a display board or interactive whiteboard before the lesson, and ask the children to read them so that they begin to notice similarities and differences between them. Then ask them to work with others to sort them into sets with similarities (see *Notes on the activities,* page 11). Continued on page 62.

100% New Developing Literacy Understanding and Responding to Texts: Ages 8–9
© A & C BLACK

Poems alike: 2

⑧ from Witch, Witch

"Witch, witch, where do you fly?"…
"Under the clouds and over the sky."

"Witch, witch, what do you eat?"…
"Little black apples from Hurricane Street."

"Witch, witch, what do you drink?"…
"Vinegar, blacking, and good red ink."

"Witch, witch, where do you sleep?"…
"Up in the clouds where pillows are cheap."

Rose Fyleman

⑨ from Iroquois Prayer

We return thanks to our mother, the earth,
    which sustains us.
We return thanks to the rivers and streams,
    which supply us with fresh water.
We return thanks to all herbs, which furnish
    Medicines for the cure of our diseases.

Anon

⑩ Pied Beauty

Glory be to God for dappled things –
    For skies of couple-colour as a brinded cow;
        For rose-moles all in stipple upon trout that swim;
Fresh-firecoal chestnut-falls; finches' wings;
    Landscape plotted and pieced – fold, fallow, and plough;
        And all trades, their gear and tackle and trim.

All things counter, original, spare, strange;
    Whatever is fickle, freckled (who knows how?)
        With swift, slow; sweet, sour; adazzle, dim;
He fathers-forth whose beauty is past change:
                        Praise him.

Gerard Manley Hopkins

⑪ Snowman

Snowman in a field
listening to the raindrops
wishing him farewell.

Roger McGough

⑫ Cousin Jane

Yesterday my cousin Jane
Said she was an aeroplane,
But I wanted further proof –
So I pushed her off the roof.

Colin West

⑬ The young girl from Goole

There was a young girl from Goole,
Who took her pet snake to school
It squiggled and wriggled
And the whole class giggled
Her teacher didn't think it was cool.

Anon

⑭ from The Doll Festival

Lighted lanterns
cast a gentle radiance
on pink peach blossoms.

James Kirkup

⑮ God be in my head

God be in my head
And in my understanding
God be in my eyes
And in my looking
God be in my mouth
And in my speaking
God be at my end
And at my departing.

Traditional, British

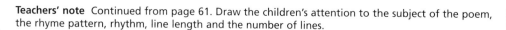

Teachers' note Continued from page 61. Draw the children's attention to the subject of the poem, the rhyme pattern, rhythm, line length and the number of lines.

100% New Developing Literacy Understanding and Responding to Texts: Ages 8–9 © A & C BLACK

Poems alike: 3

• **Record what you notice about one set of poems.**

Poem number	Subject	Rhyme pattern	Rhythm: e.g. walking, trotting, sliding, train	Numbers of lines or syllables in a verse	Type of poem: haiku, prayer, couplet, limerick

NOW TRY THIS!

• Find another example of this type of poem.
• Explain how the poems are similar.

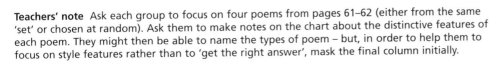

Teachers' note Ask each group to focus on four poems from pages 61–62 (either from the same 'set' or chosen at random). Ask them to make notes on the chart about the distinctive features of each poem. They might then be able to name the types of poem – but, in order to help them to focus on style features rather than to 'get the right answer', mask the final column initially.

100% New Developing Literacy
Understanding and Responding
to Texts: Ages 8–9
© A & C BLACK

63

On the wrong lines

- **Read the poems aloud.**
- **Underline the two lines in each that seem wrong.**
- **Explain what is wrong with them.**

Windy Nights

Whenever the moon and stars are set,
    Whenever the wind is high,
All night long in the dark and wet,
    A man goes riding by.
Late in the night when the fires are out,
Why does he gallop and gallop along the road?

Whenever the trees are crying aloud,
    And ships are tossed at sea,
By, on the highway, low and noisily,
    By at the gallop goes he.
By at the gallop he goes and then
By he comes back at the gallop again.

Robert Louis Stevenson

from The Mad Gardener's Song

He thought he saw an Elephant,
That practised on a fife:
He looked again, and found it was
A letter from his wife.
"At length I realise," he said,
"The bitterness of Living!"

He thought he saw a Buffalo
Upon the chimney-piece:
He looked again, and found it was
His Sister's Husband's Niece.
"Unless you leave this house," he said,
"I'll send for the fire brigade!"

Lewis Carroll

In line _____

_____

_____

_____

_____

_____

_____

In line _____

_____

_____

_____

_____

_____

_____

NOW TRY THIS!

- **Predict what the wrong lines should say.**
- **Write the new lines.**
- **Read the poems aloud.**

Do they sound better?

Teachers' note Ask the children to work with a partner: one reads aloud while the other listens. The listener could identify the 'odd' line. Ask them to make notes about why they think this line is wrong (see _Notes on the activities_, page 11, for the correct lines).

**100% New Developing Literacy
Understanding and Responding
to Texts: Ages 8–9
© A & C BLACK**